ANTHOLOGY OF SACRED SONG

CELEBRATED
ARIAS
FROM
ORATORIOS
BY OLD AND
MODERN
COMPOSERS

EDITED BY
MAX SPICKER

VOL. 1. SOPRANO
2. ALTO
→ 3. TENOR
4. BASS

ED. 524

G. SCHIRMER, *Inc.*

DISTRIBUTED BY
HAL•LEONARD® CORPORATION
7777 W. BLUEMOUND RD. P.O. BOX 13819 MILWAUKEE, WI 53213

DESIGN COPYRIGHT 1901 BY G. SCHIRMER   EDWARD B EDWARDS DES. 1901

EVANSTON PUBLIC LIBRARY
1703 ORRINGTON AVENUE
EVANSTON, ILLINOIS 60201

M782.23 Antholo
v.3
Spicker, Max, 1858-191
Anthology of sacred song
: vol. 3, tenor.
[1902]

Anthology of Sacred Song

Tenor
Index of Oratorios

	PAGE
Abraham (B. Molique)	
Aria. Pour out thy heart before the Lord	135
Athalia (G. F. Händel)	
Recit. and Aria. Gentle airs, melodious strains	52
Christmas Oratorio (J. S Bach)	
Recit. and Aria. Ye foes of man, your might is shaken	1
Creation, The (Jos. Haydn)	
Recit. and Aria. In native worth and honour clad	104
Crucifixion, The (J. Stainer)	
Aria. King ever-glorious	158
Daughter of Jairus, The (J. Stainer)	
Aria. My hope is in the Everlasting	162
Destruction of Jerusalem (F. Hiller)	
Recit. and Aria. Yes, Thou wilt yet remember	115
Elijah (F. Mendelssohn)	
Recit. and Aria. If with all your hearts ye truly seek me	118
Aria. Then shall the righteous shine forth	121
Engedi (L. van Beethoven)	
Recit. and Aria. Oh, my heart is sore within me	14
Fall of Babylon (L. Spohr)	
Recit. and Aria. Remember, Lord, what Thou hast laid upon us	152
Harvest Cantata (C. M. von Weber)	
Recit. and Aria. Happy nation, still receiving	175
Hercules (G. F. Händel)	
Aria. From celestial seats descending	55
Holy City, The (A. R. Gaul)	
Aria. My soul is athirst for God	40
Aria. To the Lord our God belong mercies	43
Hymn of Praise (F. Mendelssohn)	
Recit. and Aria. He counteth all your sorrows	124
Jephtha (G. F. Händel)	
Recit. and Aria. Waft her, angels, thro' the skies	59
Jephtha (C. Reinthaler)	
Recit. and Aria. Lovely and sweet as the rose in the vale	146
Judas Maccabæus (G. F. Händel)	
Recit. and Aria. Sound an alarm!	66
Judith (C. H. H. Parry)	
Aria. I will bear the indignation of God	138

Anthology of Sacred Song

Tenor
Index of Oratorios—Continued

	PAGE
Light of the World, The (Sir A. Sullivan)	
Aria. Refrain thy voice from weeping	167
Messiah, The (G. F. Händel)	
Recit. and Aria. Ev'ry valley shall be exalted	71
Recit. and Aria. Thou shalt break them with a rod of iron	77
Occasional Oratorio (G. F. Händel)	
Aria. Jehovah! to my words give ear	81
Prodigal Son, The (Sir A. Sullivan)	
Recit. and Aria. Come, ye children, and hearken unto me	171
Rebekah (J. Barnby)	
Recit. and Aria. The soft southern breeze plays around	9
Resurrection of Lazarus (R. Pugno)	
Recit. and Arioso. Thy name I praise, O God	142
Ruth (F. H. Cowen)	
Aria. How excellent is Thy loving-kindness	31
St. Cecilia (Sir J. Benedict)	
Aria. A wondrous change my spirit doth surprise	24
St. Paul (F. Mendelssohn)	
Cavatina. Be thou faithful unto death	128
Samson (G. F. Händel)	
Recit. and Aria. Total eclipse! no sun, no moon	86
Recit. and Aria. Why does the God of Israel sleep?	88
Seasons, The (Jos. Haydn)	
Recit. and Aria. The trav'ler stands perplex'd	109
Seed-time and Harvest (M. B. Foster)	
Recit. and Aria. Seek ye first the kingdom of God	37
Seven Last Words, The (S. Mercadante)	
Aria. When to the lily fair	131
Susanna (G. F. Händel)	
Recit. and Aria. Ye verdant hills, ye balmy vales	98
Ten Virgins, The (A. R. Gaul)	
Arioso. Ascribe unto the Lord worship and power	46
Tobias (Ch. Gounod)	
Aria. Father, thine arms about me throw!	48
Woman of Samaria, The (S. Bennett)	
Aria. His salvation is nigh them that fear Him	28

Anthology of Sacred Song

Tenor
Index of Authors

BACH, J. S. — Christmas Oratorio
- Recit. Depart! enough! my treasure I retain 1
- Aria. Ye foes of man, your might is shaken

BARNBY, J. — Rebekah
- Recit. With overflowing heart, O Lord 9
- Aria. The soft southern breeze plays around

BEETHOVEN, L. van — Engedi
- Recit. Jehovah, hear, oh hear me! 14
- Aria. Oh, my heart is sore within me

BENEDICT, Sir J. — St. Cecilia
- Aria. A wondrous change my spirit doth surprise 24

BENNETT, S. — The Woman of Samaria
- Aria. His salvation is nigh them that fear Him 28

COWEN, F. H. — Ruth
- Aria. How excellent is Thy loving-kindness 31

FOSTER, M. B. — Seed-time and Harvest
- Recit. Your heavenly Father knoweth 37
- Aria. Seek ye first the kingdom of God

GAUL, A. R. — The Holy City
- Aria. My soul is athirst for God 40
- Aria. To the Lord our God belong mercies 43

The Ten Virgins
- Arioso. Ascribe unto the Lord worship and power 46

GOUNOD, CH. — Tobias
- Aria. Father, thine arms about me throw! 48

HÄNDEL, G. F. — Athalia
- Recit. Great Queen, be calm 52
- Aria. Gentle airs, melodious strains

Hercules
- Aria. From celestial seats descending 55

Jephtha
- Recit. Deeper and deeper still 59
- Aria. Waft her, angels, thro' the skies

Judas Maccabæus
- Recit. My arms! against this Gorgias will I go 66
- Aria. Sound an alarm!

Messiah
- Recit. Comfort ye, my people 71
- Aria. Ev'ry valley shall be exalted
- Recit. He that dwelleth in heaven 77
- Aria. Thou shalt break them with a rod of iron

Occasional Oratorio
- Aria. Jehovah! to my words give ear 81

Samson
- Recit. Oh, loss of sight! 86
- Aria. Total eclipse! no sun, no moon
- Recit. My grief for this forbids mine eyes to close 88
- Aria. Why does the God of Israel sleep?

15890

Anthology of Sacred Song

Tenor
Index of Authors—Continued

HÄNDEL, G. F. Susanna
- Recit. *Tyrannic Love! I feel thy cruel dart* 98
- Aria. *Ye verdant hills, ye balmy vales*

HAYDN, JOS. The Creation
- Recit. *And God created Man* 104
- Aria. *In native worth and honour clad*

The Seasons
- Recit. *A crystal pavement lies the lake* 109
- Aria. *The trav'ler stands perplex'd*

HILLER, F. Destruction of Jerusalem
- Recit. *All my strength hath fled away* 115
- Aria. *Yes, Thou wilt yet remember*

MENDELSSOHN, F. Elijah
- Recit. *Ye people, rend your hearts* 118
- Aria. *If with all your hearts ye truly seek me*
- Aria. *Then shall the righteous shine forth* 121

Hymn of Praise
- Recit. *Sing ye praise, all ye redeemed* 124
- Aria. *He counteth all your sorrows*

St. Paul
- Cavatina. *Be thou faithful unto death* 128

MERCADANTE, S. The Seven Last Words
- Aria. *When to the lily fair* 131

MOLIQUE, B. Abraham
- Aria. *Pour out thy heart before the Lord* 135

PARRY, C. H. H. Judith
- Aria. *I will bear the indignation of God* 138

PUGNO, R. Resurrection of Lazarus
- Recit. *I live! my heart is beating!* 142
- Arioso. *Thy name I praise, O God*

REINTHALER, C. Jephtha
- Recit. *What! Miriam shall perish on the sacrificial altar?* 146
- Aria. *Lovely and sweet as the rose in the vale*

SPOHR, L. The Fall of Babylon
- Recit. *O how familiar to mine ear* 152
- Aria. *Remember, Lord, what Thou hast laid upon us*

STAINER, J. The Crucifixion
- Aria. *King ever-glorious* 158

The Daughter of Jairus
- Aria. *My hope is in the Everlasting* 162

SULLIVAN, Sir A. The Light of the World
- Aria. *Refrain thy voice from weeping* 167

The Prodigal Son
- Recit. *No chastening for the present seemeth joyous* 171
- Aria. *Come, ye children, and hearken unto me*

WEBER, C. M. von Harvest Cantata
- Recit. *Look how the fruitful land is smiling* 175
- Aria. *Happy nation, still receiving*

15830

Anthology of Sacred Song

Christmas Oratorio.
Recitative and Aria.

J. S. BACH.

Depart! enough, my treasure I retain, With me He doth remain, And while I live will not forsake me, He to His kind embrace With soft and gentle grace And sweetest tenderness will take me. Now as my bridegroom I receive Him, And all my heart's de-vo-tion give Him; Full well I know, He lov-eth me, And I, too, love Him hear-ti-ly, And for His hon-or live. What foe from me this joy can rend, That He vouch-safes to give? Thou, Je-sus, art my con-stant friend, And in dis-tress I cry to Thee, Lord, help, Lord, help, my shield and succor be.

Aria.
Andante con moto. (♩= 63)

Ye foes of man, your might is shaken, Dismay no more in me ye waken, My strength, my shield is ev-er near, my strength, my shield is near, is near. Ye foes of man, your might is shaken, Dismay no more in me ye waken; My strength, my shield is near, my strength, my shield is ever near.

poco largamente
col canto
energico
a tempo

p un poco agitato ... *cresc.*

What though with fear ye strive to fill me, And threaten

sempre cresc.

in your rage to kill me? Behold, my Saviour dwelleth

f

here, behold, my Saviour dwelleth here.

What though with fear ye strive to fill me, And threaten in your rage to kill me? Behold, my Saviour dwelleth here, behold, my Saviour dwelleth here.

7

cresc.
con forza
near,— is near, my strength, my shield— is ev - er near,— my
cresc.
p rallent.
Adagio
f
strength, my— shield is— ev - er— near, my strength, my shield is
col canto
f col canto
ev - er near.
Tempo I.
marcato

Rebekah.
Recitative and Aria.

J. BARNBY.

ing; Un-to Thy throne her many-voiced anthem Nature lifts; my grateful soul shall swell the song of praise.

Aria.
Allegretto. (♩ = 92)

The soft southern breeze plays around me, The birds trill their eventide song; The leaves of the wild trees make music, The waters flow murmuring along. Creation adores Thee, O Father, Its myriad soft voices outpour, To thy throne a sweet song of thanksgiving In melodious numbers doth soar, in melodious num-

-ber doth soar.

I bow me, Almighty, before Thee, I also would worship and praise, And thank Thee, O Lord, for thy goodness, That blesseth my manhood's first days.

Guide my foot-steps, pro-tect me, O Fa- - ther, My strong help and buck-ler still be, And when the death-an-gels shall call me, Let me live blest for ev-er with Thee, let me live blest for ev - er with Thee.

Engedi.[*]

Recitative and Aria.

L. v. BEETHOVEN.

Je-ho-vah, hear! oh hear me! Thou art my hope; oh Lord, de-liv-er me! Stretch forth Thy hand to help me in my trouble.

I bless Thy ho-ly name, Thou art my ref-uge and my shield; In Thee a-lone I trust.

Allegro. (♩= 138.)

[*] The music to "Engedi" has been adapted from Beethoven's "Christ on the Mount of Olives."

Maestoso. (♩=88.)
Recit.
How awful is Thy wrath, oh God of Israel!
Allegro.
Arise, oh Lord! and let thine en-emies be_ scatter'd and flee be-fore Thee.
cresc.
Maestoso. (♩=88.)
ff
sf
fp
p espress.
Oh Father! hear and grant Thy servant's pray'r, who bends before Thy Throne in sorrow, for my foes have sought my life.
cresc.
Allegro.
Adagio, a tempo. tranquillo
p
Re-member our re-proach,
agitato poco a
where-with Thine

16

poco

en - emies have reproach'd Thy ser - vants; a - rise, oh God of Hosts, *cresc.* forsake me not!

Adagio agitato. ($\flat$ = 88.)

Be- hold! how fear-ful-ly the pains of death op-

cresc.

Adagio molto. ($\flat$ = 80.)

press and wound my soul. My heart is faint, my

17

molto cresc.

Fa - ther! Be - hold! my heart is faint, have mer - cy, Lord!

sf *cresc.* *ff* *col canto* *p*

Aria.
Allegro. (♩= 120.)

p

cresc.

poco p

Oh! my

fz *ff* *p*

heart is sore within me, and my spirit, and my spirit faints away; Terrors seize me, and in darkness I am dwelling night and day. Like the shadow that declineth Are my days, my days with con - - stant fears; I am wea-ry with my groaning, And my eyes are dim with tears, and my eyes are dim, dim with tears. Fa-ther! Lord! in pain and

sempre agitato

dim.

cresc.

con molto sentimento

molto cantabile

sorrow, Lo! Thy servant prays to Thee, to Thee! For Thy power is unbounded: Lord! Lord, arise, deliver me!

Lord, arise, deliver me!

Oh, my heart is sore within me, And my spirit faints a-

cresc.
f
dim.
way, and my spir - it faints a - way,
cresc.
f
p
f
p
I am wea - - ry with my
p
groaning, I am wea - ry with my groaning,
p
And my eyes, and my eyes are dim with
cresc.
cresc.
tears, and my eyes are dim, dim with tears.
p
dim.
f
p
p

p tranquillo e con calore
Fa - ther, Lord! in
dolce
p
pain and sor - row, Lo! Thy ser - vant prays to Thee,
cresc.
p
cresc.
poco riten.
p
mf a tempo
cresc.
f
now prays to Thee, For Thy pow'r, for Thy pow'r, for Thy pow'r is un -
col canto
p
p
f
f
mf
bounded: Lord, a - rise, de - liv - er me,
ff
p
sf

mf
Lord, a - rise, de - liv - er me. Oh
sf
sf
p
sf
p
p
mf
f
Father! Lord! Lord! Lord! a - rise, de -
cresc.
p
mf
sf
sf p
cresc.
stentato
sf
liv - - er me, Lord, arise, de - liv -
f
cresc.
f
f
a piacere
- - - - er me.
p
pp

St. Cecilia.

Aria.

Sir J. BENEDICT.

A wondrous change my spirit doth surprise, Where are the clouds that lately sealed mine eyes? What care I now for all those pleasures vain That lately bound my soul in golden chain? What care I now for all those pleasures vain That bound my soul in gold-en chain? Vi-sions of Heav'n un-fold as dawn-eth day, Ce-les-tial voic-es teach me I should pray, I should pray To One, to One who giv-eth life and heal-eth grief. If I have

26

care I now for pleasures vain That lately bound, that bound my soul in golden chain? If I have sinned, if I have sinned, Almighty One, forgive! Teach me Thy will, let me begin to live; Lord, I believe, Lord, I believe, help Thou mine unbelief!

The Woman of Samaria.
Aria.

S. BENNETT.

Larghetto. (♩=80.)

His salvation is nigh them that fear Him, that glory may dwell in our land; His salvation is nigh them that fear Him, that glory may dwell in our land, may dwell in our land. Yea, the Lord shall shew loving-kindness, the Lord, the

Lord shall shew lov-ing-kindness, shall shew lov-ing-kindness, and our land shall give her increase, shall give her increase, shall give her increase. His sal-va-tion is nigh them that fear Him, His sal-va-tion-is nigh them that fear Him, that glo-ry may dwell in our

cresc.
sf
land; His sal - va - tion is nigh, is — nigh to them, is
sf
p
cresc.
sf
sf
nigh to them that fear Him, is nigh — to them, — to
sf
sf
them that fear — Him, is nigh — to them that
fear — Him.
sempre calando

Ruth.

Aria.

F. H. COWEN.

*) From sign ✥ to ✥ may be omitted.
15830

Poco più lento.

mf quasi recit. *dim.*

How ex-cel-lent is Thy lov-ing-kind-ness, O God!

Tempo I. ($\quarter = 100$)

Thou vis-it-est the earth, and mak-est it soft with show'rs.

Thou crown-est the year with Thy good-ness, Thou crown-est the year with Thy good-ness, Thou crownest the year with Thy good-ness, and Thy paths drop fat - - ness.

They drop up-on the pas-tures of the wil - der-ness, and the little hills are gird-ed with joy. The val - leys al - so are covered o-ver with corn, they shout for joy, they shout for joy, and

Poco più animato. (♩ = 120.)

largamente

colla voce

sing. God hath giv-en me of the dew of heaven, and the fat-ness of the earth, and the fat-ness of the earth, and plen-ty of corn and wine. How ex-cel-lent is Thy lov-ing-kind-ness; Thou vis-it-est the earth, Thou vis-it-est the earth and makest it soft, and mak-est it soft with show'rs. The hills are gird-ed with joy, the valleys are covered, are cov-ered o-ver with corn, they shout for joy, they shout for joy, they shout for joy, and sing, they shout for joy, for joy,

36

Seed-time and Harvest.

Recitative and Aria.

M. B. FOSTER.

Your heav'nly Father knoweth that ye have need of all these things, your heav'nly Father knoweth; I therefore say unto you: Seek ye first the kingdom of God, and His righteousness, seek ye first the kingdom of God,

38

eat, or what ye shall drink, but seek ye first the kingdom of God, and His righteousness, seek ye first the kingdom of God, and all these things shall be added unto you. Seek ye first the kingdom, the kingdom of God.

The Holy City.
Aria.

A. R. GAUL.

Andantino religioso. (♩= 76.)

p cantabile

p espress.

My soul is a-thirst for God, yea, e'en for the liv - ing God; When shall I come, come to appear be - fore the presence of God?

p lugubre

My tears have been my meat day and

41

out, out of my trouble: O bring Thou me out of my trouble, my troub-le. My soul is a-thirst for God, yea, e'en for the liv-ing God; When shall I come, come to ap-pear be-fore the pres-ence, the pres-ence of God?

The Holy City.

Aria.

A. R. GAUL.

Andante religioso.

espress.
For like as a father pitieth his children, even so is the Lord merciful to them that fear Him.
dim.
For like as a father pitieth his children, even so is the Lord merciful to them that fear Him,
cresc.
merciful to them that fear Him, to them that fear
that fear,

45

The Ten Virgins.
Arioso.

A. R. GAUL.

Andante con moto. ($\quarter=88$)

A-scribe un-to the Lord, O ye kin-dreds of the peo-ple, a-scribe un-to the Lord wor-ship and power, a-scribe un-to the Lord, ye kin-dreds of the peo-ple, a-scribe un-to the Lord wor-ship and power.

47

Tobias.
Aria.

CH. GOUNOD.

gladness, not of sor - row! Then let the glad tears flow, They tell of joy, not sorrow, let them flow! And Fa - ther! lo! anoth-er son, Tho' to thee yet a stranger! Faith - ful and true to me in dan - ger! Still he guided my steps,— And the ref-uge was won! When lost in des-ert wild, of my home I was dreaming, From

care, from care all my sad soul re-deem-ing. Moth-er! Moth-er! It was he calm'd thy child! From his care, from his longing, 'Twas he re-deemed thy child! Ah! Fa-ther, thine arms a-bout me throw, Moth-er! thou wilt not let me go. Fair will dawn now life's morrow, fair will dawn now life's morrow; What though your eyes brim o'er, 'tis joy, not sor-row! Then let the glad tears gen-tly flow, then let the glad tears gen-tly flow, Your brimming eyes are tell-ing Of joy, not sor-row, let the glad tears flow. Fa-ther! thine arms a-bout me throw! Moth-er! thou wilt not let me go! O fa-ther mine! O fa-ther mine! A-bout me still thine old arms throw!

Athalia.
Recitative and Aria.
(With Violoncello obbligato.)

G. F. HÄNDEL.

Recit.

Great Queen! be calm, these fears I deem The birth of a delusive dream; Let Harmony breathe soft around, For sadness ceases at the sound.

Aria.
Largo. (♪=72)

Violoncello Solo
cantabile

cresc.

dolce ed espress.

Gentle airs, melodious strains, Call for raptures out of

53

*) Cadenza in brackets [ ] may be omitted.

Hercules.
Aria.

G. F. HÄNDEL.

Larghetto alla Siciliana.

From celestial seats descending, Joys divine a-while suspending, Gods have left their Heav'n above, gods have left their Heav'n above, To taste the sweeter heav'n of love, to taste the sweeter heav'n of love, to taste the sweeter heav'n of love. From celestial seats descending, Joys divine a-while suspending,

Gods have left their Heav'n a-bove, To taste the sweeter heav'n of love, to taste the heav'n of love, Gods have left their Heav'n a-bove, To taste the sweeter heav'n of love, to taste, to taste the sweet-er heav'n of love.

Cease my passion then to blame, Cease to scorn a god-like

cresc.
f
flame, cease to scorn a god-like flame, a god-like flame, cease to scorn a god-like flame, Cease my
cresc.
poco allargando
p a tempo
pas-sion then to blame, Cease — to scorn — a god - like flame. From ce-
col canto
dim.
p
p
cresc
mf
lestial seats descending, Joys di-vine a-while sus-pending, Gods have left their Heav'n a-
p
mp
cresc.
bove, Gods have left their Heav'n a - bove, To taste the sweeter heav'n of love, to taste the sweeter heav'n of
espress.
mf
love, to taste the sweet - er heav'n — of love. From ce-
mf
dim.

lestial seats descending, Joys divine awhile suspending, Gods have left their Heav'n a-bove To taste the sweeter heav'n of love, to taste the heav'n of love, Gods have left their Heav'n a-bove, To taste the sweet-er heav'n of love, to taste, to taste the sweet-er heav'n of love. *a tempo*

Jephtha.

Recitative and Aria.

G. F. HÄNDEL.

Largo. (♩= 72.) **Recit.**

Deeper, and deeper still, thy goodness, child, Pierceth a father's bleeding heart, and checks the cruel sentence on my falt'ring tongue. Oh! let me whisper it to the raging winds, Or howling desert; for the ears of men

Nº 1. "Deeper, and deeper still!"— This Recitative, though usually so sung, was not intended by Händel to precede the Aria, but is placed in an earlier part of the Oratorio, immediately before the Chorus, "How dark, O Lord, are Thy decrees."

15830

It is too shocking. Yet, have I not vow'd? And can I think the great Jehovah sleeps, Like Chemosh, and such fabled deities? Ah! no! Heav'n heard my thoughts, and wrote them down. It must be so. 'Tis this that racks my brain, And pours into my breast a thousand

f
pangs, That lash me in-to madness.
Largo
Hor - rid
mf
f f
p
thought! hor-rid thought!
p con calore
My on-ly daughter! So
p
p dim.
pp
stretto
f deciso
dear a child, Doom'd by a fa-ther! Yes, the vow is
pp
p
past, And Gil - e - ad hath triumph'd o'er his foes. There-fore,
f
f f
dim.
p
pp morendo
to-morrow's dawn_ to-morrow's dawn_ I can no more!
p
ten.
p
pp
pp

Aria.

Andante larghetto. (♩= 84.)

mp dolce

p sosten. con tenerezza

Waft her, angels, thro' the skies,

cresc. *p* *p dolce*

waft her, an-gels, thro' the skies, Far a-bove yon a-zure

p tranquillo

plain, far a-bove yon a-zure plain.

An - gels, waft her thro' the skies, waft her thro' the skies, Far a-bove yon a-zure plain, far a-bove yon a-zure plain; Glo-rious there, like you, to rise, There, like you, for ev - er reign, Glo-rious there, like you, to rise, _____ There, like you, for ev - er reign, for ev - er reign, _____ there, like you, for ev - er reign.

Waft her, an-gels, thro' the skies, waft her, an-gels, thro' the skies, Far a-bove yon a-zure plain, far a-bove yon a-zure plain.

tranquillo

An - gels, waft her thro' the skies, waft her thro' the skies, Far a-bove yon a - zure plain, _____ far a-

allarg.

bove yon a - - zure plain.

Judas Maccabaeus.
Recitative and Aria.

G. F. HÄNDEL.

Recit.

My arms! A-gainst this Gorgias will I go. The I-du-me-an gov-er-nor shall know How vain, how in-ef-fective his design, While rage his leader, and Je-ho-vah mine.

Aria.
Allegro con spirito.

Sound an a-larm! sound an a-larm, your sil-ver trum-pets sound, And call the brave, and on-ly brave, and on-ly brave a-round, call the brave, call the brave, and on-ly brave around. Sound an a-larm! Your sil-ver trumpets sound, your trumpets sound, your trumpets sound, And call the brave, and on-ly brave, and call the brave and on-ly brave, and on-ly brave a-round, call the brave, call the brave,

stentato
and only brave, a-round.
a tempo
col canto
f
mf
Who list-eth, fol-low;
p
to the field a-gain.
marcato
Justice with courage, is a thou-sand
cresc.
mf
men, is a thousand men, Jus-tice with courage, Justice with courage is a
f
largamente
thou-sand men, is a thou-sand men, is a thou - sand men.
col canto

Aria.
Tempo I.

Sound an a-larm! Sound an a-larm, your sil-ver trumpets sound! And call the brave, and on-ly brave, and on-ly brave, a-round. Sound an a-larm!

Your silver trumpets sound, And call the brave, and only brave, and only brave, and only brave, around!

The Messiah.
Recitative and Aria.

Isaiah XI, 1, 2, 3.

G. F. HÄNDEL.

Larghetto. (♪ = 80.)

Recit. Com-fort ye, com- - fort ye, ___ my people, com- - fort ye, com- - fort ye my people, saith your God; saith your God; speak ye com-fort-a-bly to Je-ru-sa-lem, speak ye com-fort-a-bly to Je-

15830

mf
poco riten.
p
a tempo
ru-sa-lem, and cry un-to her that her war- -fare, her
mf
p
cresc.
stentato
war - fare is ac-complished, that her in-i-qui-ty is pardon'd, that her in-
cresc.
dim.
p
(tr)
i-qui-ty is par-don'd.
f
f a piacere
con forza e ben marcato
The voice of him that crieth in the wil-der-ness, "Pre- pare ye the way of the
f
Lord, make straight in the de-sert a high-way for our God."

Aria.
Andante. (♪ = 88)

Ev-'ry val - ley, ev - 'ry val - ley shall be ex - alt-ed, shall be ex - alt -

74

75

p
- - - - -ed, and ev-'ry mountain and hill made low, the
tr
crooked straight, the crook-ed straight, the crooked straight, and the
p
cresc.
rough places plain, and the rough plac-es plain, and the rough places
f
a piacere
Adagio.
plain, the crook-ed straight, and the rough
m.s.
colla voce
Tempo I.
plac - es plain.

The Messiah.
Recitative and Aria.

Psalm II, 4.

G. F. HÄNDEL.

He that dwelleth in heaven shall laugh them to scorn; the Lord shall have them in derision.

Aria. Andante. (♩ = 92.)

Psalm II, 9.

Thou shalt break them, Thou shalt

sempre con
break them with a rod of i - ron, Thou shalt
forza
dash them in piec - es like a pot - ter's ves - sel, Thou shalt
cresc.
dash them in piec - es, in piec - es, like a pot -
ter's ves - sel,
energico
Thou shalt

break them, Thou shalt break them with a
mf
rod of i - ron,
p
mf
Thou shalt dash them in piec-es like_ a_ pot - - -
p
cresc.
cresc.
- - ters_ ves-sel, Thou shalt dash them in
cresc.
cresc.
mf
molto cresc.
f
piec-es like a pot - - - - - ter's ves-sel, like a

80

pot - - ter's ves - sel, Thou shalt dash them in piec - es like a pot - - ter's ves - sel.

Occasional Oratorio.
Aria
(with Violoncello obbligato).

G. F. HÄNDEL.

ho - vah! to my words_ give_ ear,
Solo
poco cresc.
to my words_ give_ ear, My med - i - ta - tions weigh, Je - ho - vah! Je
Solo
mf
p
mf
mp
ho - vah! my med - i - ta - tions weigh!
con anima
Solo
p
mf
The
cresc.
m.d. m.s. m.d.
mp

voice of my com-plain-ing hear, To Thee a-lone, my God and King, to Thee I pray, to Thee a-lone, my God and King, I pray.

The voice of my com-

plain - ing hear, To Thee a - lone, my
p
mf
Solo
p
cresc.
God and King, to Thee I pray, to Thee a-lone, my God and
cresc.
King, I pray, to Thee a - lone,
p
più lento
my God and King, I pray.
Tempo I.
dim.
col canto
mf
Solo
Solo

+) The Cadenza from [to] may be omitted.

Samson.
Recitative and Aria.

G. F. HÄNDEL.

Recit. Oh, loss of sight! of thee I most complain! Oh, worse than beggary, old age, or chains! my very soul in real darkness dwells.

Aria. Larghetto. ($\eighthnote = 96$)

Total eclipse! no sun, no moon, All dark, all dark amidst the blaze of noon! O, glo-rious light! no cheering ray To glad my eyes with wel-come day!

Total e-clipse! no sun, no moon, All dark amidst the blaze of noon! Why thus depriv'd Thy prime decree? Sun, moon and stars are dark to me, sun, moon and stars, sun, moon and stars are dark to me, sun, moon and stars, sun, moon and stars are dark to me!

Samson.
Recitative and Aria.

G. F. HÄNDEL.

Aria.
Allegro. (♩=84)

Why does the God of Israel sleep?

con spirito
A-rise with dread-ful sound, a-

rise, a-rise, a-rise with dreadful sound, a-rise with dread-ful sound, with dread-ful sound, a-rise, a-rise with dreadful sound, with dread-ful sound, a-rise, a-rise, a-rise with dreadful sound, with dreadful sound, With clouds en-com-pass'd round;   with clouds en-com-pass'd round;

Then shall the hea-then hear Thy thun-der, then shall the hea-then hear Thy thun-der, Thy thun-der deep.

tem-pest of Thy wrath now raise, In whirl-winds them pur-sue, Full fraught with ven-geance due, In whirl-winds them pur-sue, in

93

94

till shame, till shame and trou-ble, till shame and trou-ble all Thy foes shall seize, till shame and trou-ble all Thy foes shall seize, till shame and trou-ble all

allarg.
a tempo
f
thy foes shall seize.
mf
Why
a piacere
does the God of Israel sleep?
p a tempo
cresc.
A-
con spirito
rise with dreadful sound, a-rise, a-rise, a-rise with dreadful sound, With
clouds en-com-pass'd round, en-com-pass'd

round, Then shall the hea-then hear Thy thun - der deep. The tem - pest of Thy wrath now raise, In whirl - winds them pur - sue, them pur-sue, Full fraught with ven - geance due, Till shame and trouble, till shame and

trouble all _____ Thy foes shall seize,

till shame and trouble all Thy

foes__ shall seize!

Susanna.
Recitative and Aria.

G. F. HÄNDEL.

Tyrannic Love! I feel thy cruel dart, Nor age protects me from the burning smart. What! seated with the Elders of the land To guide stern Justice' unrelenting hand, Shall I submit, shall I submit to feel the raging fires? Youth pleads a warrant for his hot de-

sires, But when the blood should scarce at-tempt to flow, I feel the pur-ple torrents fiercely glow: Love conquers all, a-las! I find it so. Bear me re-sist-less down the rap-id tide; No faith-ful pi-lot shall my ves-sel guide, No friend-ly star her gen-tle light supplies! But pitch-y clouds in-volve the darken'd skies! The tem-pest howls! the foam-ing surg-es roar! While I, un-hap-py, quit the saf-er shore.

Aria.
Larghetto. (♩ = 80)

Ye ver-dant hills, ye

balm-y vales, Bear wit-ness of my pains! How oft have Shi-nar's flow'r-y dales Been taught my am-'rous strains! The wound-ed oaks in yon-der grove Re-tain the name of her I love; The wounded oaks in yon-der grove Re-tain the name of her I love.

In vain would age his

ice be-spread To numb each gay de-sire, Though seven-ty win-ters hoar my head, My heart is still on fire. By moss-y fount and grot I rove, And gen-tly mur-mur songs of love; By moss-y fount and grot I rove, And gen-tly mur-mur songs of love.

Oh! sweet-est of thy love-ly race, Un-

103

The Creation.
Recitative and Aria.

JOS. HAYDN.

And God cre-a-ted Man in his own im-age, In the im-age of God cre-a-ted he him; Male and fe-male cre-a-ted he them. He breath-ed in-to his nos-trils the breath of life, and Man be-came a liv-ing soul.

Aria.
Andante.

In

native worth and honour clad, With beauty, courage, strength adorn'd, Erect with front serene he stands, A Man, the Lord and King of nature all. His large and arched brow sublime Of wisdom deep declares the seat; And in his eyes with brightness

106

With fond-ness leans up-on his breast The part-ner for him form'd, A wo-man, fair and grace-ful spouse, a woman, fair and grace-ful spouse. Her soft-ly smil-ing vir-gin looks, Of flow'r-y spring the mir-ror, Be-speak him love,

108

The Seasons.
Recitative and Aria.

JOS. HAYDN.

A crys-tal pave-ment lies the lake; Ar-rest-ed stands the ra-pid stream; And o'er the lof-ty cliff the tor-rent hangs With i-dle threat and seeming roar. The leaf-less woods no more re-sound, The fields are hid, the val-leys chok'd, With heaps im-mense of drift-ed snow; The drea-ry earth ap-pears a grave, Where Nature's splendour lies conceal'd; A death-like hue o'er all prevails, And o'er the wild and bleak expanse Pale Desolation spreads her wings.

Aria.
Presto. ($\quarter = 166$)

The trav'ler stands per-plex'd, For-lorn, un-cer-tain he, Which way his wan-d'ring, wan-d'ring steps to turn, to turn A-cross the trackless waste. No hu-man dwell-ing cheers his sight, No mark of human foot is found, no mark of hu-man foot is found;

111

agitato e più cresc.

No human dwelling cheers his sight, No mark, no mark of foot is found, no mark of human foot is found;

And onward as he bravely toils, In deeper er-ror plung-es still, in deeper er-ror plunges still, in deep - er er - ror plung - es still.

p più tranquillo

De-press'd, his cour - age sinks, And an - guish wrings his

15830

heart, As night its sable horrors sheds, And weariness and cold Have stiffen'd all his limbs. Depress'd his courage sinks, And anguish wrings his heart! Before his glad-den'd sight appears A sudden gleam of neighb'ring light; And now reviv'd he springs,

With joyful panting breast, with joyful panting breast,

cantabile
To gain the door, to gain the welcome, welcome door,

p poco riten.
Where all his pains may find relief! *a tempo*

mf a tempo *cresc.*
And now, reviv'd, he springs With joy-

-ful, with joyful panting breast, with joyful panting breast,

To gain the door, to gain the welcome, wel-come door, to gain the wel-come door, Where all his pains may find re-lief, may find re-lief, may find re-lief.

The Destruction of Jerusalem.

Recitative and Aria.

F. HILLER.

All my strength hath fled a-way, and all I hoped for from the Lord. Re-mem-ber, Lord, that we are wretch-ed and for-sa-ken, re-mem-ber, Lord, that we are wretched and for-sa-ken, re-mem-ber, Lord!

Aria. Andante con moto.

Yes, Thou wilt yet re-mem-ber, e'en thus my soul doth an-swer me; yes,

15830

Thou wilt yet re-mem-ber, e'en thus my soul doth an-swer me; so shall my heart find com-fort, and still shall trust in Thee, so shall my heart find com-fort, and still shall trust in Thee. Yes, Thou wilt yet re-mem-ber, thus my soul doth an-swer me, ___ thus my soul doth answer me; so shall __ my heart find com- fort, and shall trust, __ shall trust in Thee, __ yes, Thou __ wilt yet re- mem- ber, thus my __ soul doth __ an- swer me, ___ and shall trust __ in Thee, __ and shall trust __ in Thee. ___

Elijah.
Recitative and Aria.
F. MENDELLSOHN.

Ye peo-ple, rend your hearts, rend your hearts, and not your garments for your transgressions: e-ven as E-li-jah hath sealed the heavens through the word of God. I there-fore say to ye, Forsake your idols, return to God; for He is slow to anger, and mer-ciful, and kind, and gracious, and re-penteth Him of the e-vil.

Aria.
Andante con moto. (♩ = 72.)

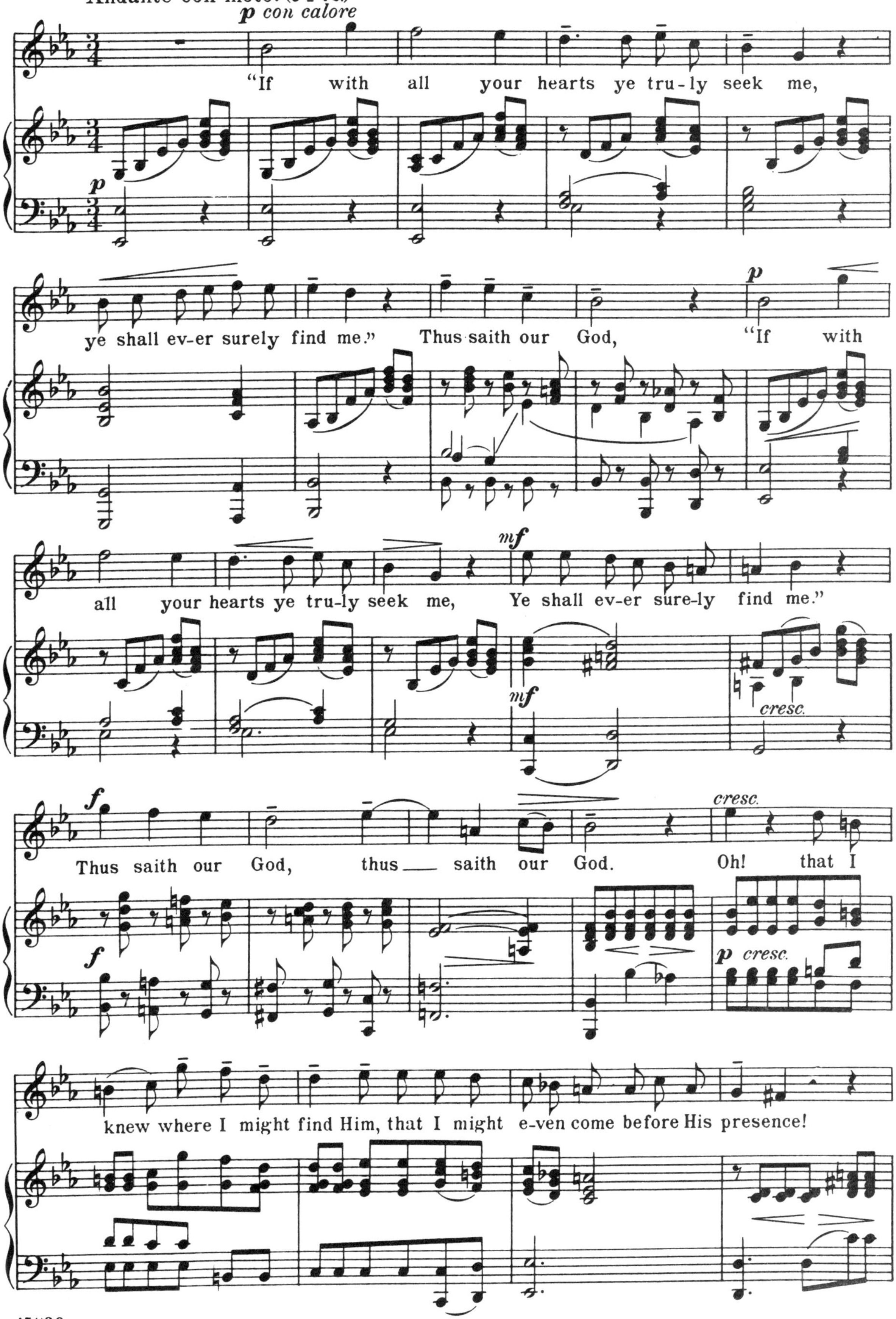

Oh! that I knew where I might find Him, that I might e-ven come before His presence! come before His presence! Oh! that I knew where I might find Him! "If with all your hearts ye truly seek me, Ye shall ev-er sure-ly find me." Thus saith our God. "Ye shall ever surely find me." Thus saith our God.

Elijah.
Aria.
F. MENDELSSOHN.

Then, then shall the righteous shine forth as the sun in their heav'nly Father's realm, shine forth as the sun in their heav'nly Father's realm, then shall the righteous shine forth in their heav'nly Father's realm, as the sun, as the sun in their heav'nly Father's

realm. Joy on their head shall be for ev-er-lasting, joy on their head shall be for ev-er-last-ing, and all sor-row and mourn-ing shall flee a-way, shall flee a-way for ev - er. Then, then shall the right-eous shine forth as the sun in their heav'n-ly Fa - ther's realm, shine forth, shine in their heav'n-ly Fa-ther's realm,

shine forth as the sun in their heav'n-ly Fa-ther's realm, then shall the right-eous

shine in their heav'n-ly Fa-ther's realm.

Hymn of Praise.

Recitative and Aria.

F. MENDELSSOHN.

Sing ye praise, all ye redeem-ed of the Lord, redeem-ed from the hand of the foe, from your dis-tress-es, from deep af-flic-tion, who sat in the shadow of death and darkness. All ye that cry in trouble un-to the Lord, Sing ye praise! give ye thanks, pro-claim a-loud his good-ness.

Aria.
Allegro moderato. ($\quarternote$ = 80.)

espress.

He counteth all your sor-rows in the time of need. He com-forts the be-reav-ed ___ with His re-gard, He comforts the be-reav-ed, He com-forts the be-reav-ed, He com-forts the be-reav-ed with His re-gard, with His_ re-gard. He counteth all your

p
sor - rows in the time of need, He com-forts the be -
p
sf
cresc.
mf
reav - ed, He com-forts the be - reav - ed with His re -
cresc.
cresc.
p
gard, with His re - gard. He
sf
f
sf
p
count-eth all your sor - rows in the time of need, He
cresc.
cresc.
f
com-forts the be - reav - ed, He com-forts the be - reav - ed with
sf
sf

stentato
sf
p
His re - gard, with His re - gard, He
cresc.
f
com - - forts them with His re - gard, He
dim.
com - forts the be - reav - - ed, He com -
- forts them with His re - gard. Sing ye praise!
un poco rall.
Give ye thanks, pro - claim a - loud His good - - ness!

St. Paul.
Cavatina.

Rev. ii, 10; Jer. i, 8.

F. MENDELSSOHN.

Adagio. ($\quarter = 88$.)

p dolce ed espress.

Be — thou faith-ful un-to death, — and I will give to thee a crown of life, — be — thou faith-ful un-to death, — and I will give to thee a crown, a crown of life, and I will give to thee, to thee a crown of life.

Be not afraid, be not afraid, My help is nigh, be not afraid, be not afraid, My help is nigh, be not afraid, My help is nigh, be not afraid. Be thou faithful unto death, and I will give to thee, give to thee a crown of life. Be not a-fraid, My help is nigh, My help is nigh, be not a-fraid, My help is nigh.

Be thou faith-ful un-to death.

The seven last words.
Aria.

Andante mosso.

S. MERCADANTE.

pp delicatissimo

pp dolcissimo

When to the lil-y fair, Pur-est of flow-ers, Heav'n, at de-cline of day, Fresh dew de-nies, Sad-ly its droop-ing leaves Pine for the show-ers: Ah! in the sun's hot ray, Ah!

it with - ers, it with - ers and dies!

With un - told mis - e - ry, Tor - ment and an - guish,

Thirst - ed up - on the cross Our Sav - iour dear! Where is the

heart so cold, Where is the heart so cold, Can see him

133

languish, can see him languish And for his agony Deny a tear? Where is the heart so cold, where is the heart so cold? and for his agony deny a tear, and for his agony, and for his agony deny a tear?

With untold mis-e-ry, Tor-ment and an-guish, Thirst-ed up-on the cross Our Sav-iour dear; with untold mis-e-ry, Tor-ment and an-guish, Thirst-ed up-on the cross Our Sav-iour, our Sav-iour, on the cross, our Sav-iour dear!

Abraham.
Aria.

B. MOLIQUE.

Allegro moderato. (𝅗𝅥 = 80.)

Pour out thy heart before the Lord, and lift thy hands un-to Him, for He will not despise the afflicted and them that are of a broken heart. Pour out thy heart before the Lord, lift up thy hands unto Him, for He will not despise the afflicted and them that are of a broken heart. But

though He cause grief, but though He cause grief, yet will He have com-pas-sion, yet will He have com-pas-sion, ac-cord-ing to the mul-ti-tude of His mer-cies, ac-cord-ing to the mul-ti-tude of His mer-cies. But though He cause grief, yet will He have com-pas-sion! Pour out thy heart before the

Lord, and lift thy hands unto Him, for He will not despise the afflicted and them that are of a broken heart. Trust in the Lord, and He will strengthen thee, trust in the Lord, in the Lord, He will strengthen thee.

Judith.
Aria.
"The Repentance of Manasseh."

Lento espressivo. (♩ = 72.)

C. H. H. PARRY.

I will bear, will bear the indignation of God, because I have sinned, have sinned against Him, because I have sinned, sinned against Him, have sinned against Him. The Lord hath sore corrected me, But He hath not given me o-

140

-ver un-to death, He hath not giv-en me o-ver un-to death. I will wait, will wait for the sal-va-tion of God, For He will hear, will hear and de-liv-er me. He shall bring me forth, shall bring me forth in-to the light, And I shall be-hold, shall be-hold His right-eous-ness,

I shall be-hold His right-eous-ness. Then will I praise Him all the days of my life, Ev'n as the heav'ns do praise Him, Whose glo-ry shall be for ev-er-more.

The Resurrection of Lazarus.
"The Resurrection!"

English version by Dr. Th. Baker.

Moderato. *cantabile e molto sostenuto*

R. PUGNO.

Recit.
I live, my heart is beat-ing! 'Tis no vain de-lu-sion!

molto cresc. poco a poco a tempo
In the balm-y air I wan-der, I am breath-ing, I

largamente
see the sky so fair!

a tempo
molto legato
sostenuto
Thy name I praise, O God of mer-cy un-end-ing!
p a tempo
con calore
Thy name I praise, Thou Spir-it of light! O Fount tran-scending Of life, of love, and of joy,
cantabile
Thy name I praise! Thy name I praise!
O God, God of mer-cy un-end-
rit.

Un poco animato.
mf sostenuto
ing! May my hymn of re -
6 cresc. 6
6 6
mf
joic - - ing, Grate - - ful to Thee a -
cresc.
cresc.
f con gran' espressione
ris - - ing, May my hymn of re -
f
poco dim.
joic - - ing, Grate - - ful to Thee a -
allarg.
ris - - - - ing,
allarg.

con forza
O - - ver - soar the bounds of cre -
ff
a - tion Toward Thine a - bode, O-ver-
riten.
soar the bounds of cre - a - tion Toward Thy di -
largamente
col canto
largamente
molto cresc.
ff
vine a-bode on high!
molto cresc.
ff

Jephtha.

Recitative and Aria.

English version by
Dr. Th. Baker.

C. RHEINTHALER.

What! Miriam shall perish on sacrificial altar? She shall go down to the tomb, a victim of vows hastily spoken? May the Lord stretch forth His arm, and consume the hand with fire, that dares the deed!

Aria.
Andante con moto.

dolce e cantabile

dolce

Love-ly and sweet as the rose in the vale, Her eye so clear as beam-ing skies,

So came she down from the mountain-height, With joy-ful dancing her fa-ther to welcome, from the moun-tain-height, With joy-ful danc-ing her fa-ther to welcome, with joy-ful danc-ing her fa-ther to wel-come.

poco rall.

148

And as the birds' gay car-ols de-light, Sound-ed her song, sound-ed her song; And as the birds' gay car-ols de-light, Sound-ed her song, sound-ed her song.

Allegro moderato.
un poco agitato

And she now shall perish, in youthful beauty?

più agitato e cresc.

She now shall fall like the grass of Spring-tide?

Andante maestoso.
con spirito

Ye mountains of Gilboa, and ye hills round about, ye mountains of Gilboa, and ye hills round a-

Tempo I.
bout, No dew should ev - er wet ye, nor rain fall a -
fp f fp f fp f
gain, no dew should ev - er wet ye, nor rain fall a -
fp f fp f fp f fp f
f
gain, If such a deed, if such a deed may
fp cresc. f sf sf
f molto agitato
be! Ye moun - tains of Gil - bo - a, ye
p f p

hills round about, No dew shall ever wet ye, Nor rain fall again, If such a deed, if such a deed may be, if such a deed, if such a deed, if such a deed may be!

Allegro agitato.

The Fall of Babylon.
Recitative and Aria.

L. SPOHR.

O! how familiar to mine ear are these deep sounds of sorrow! Jerusalem, the stranger hath despoil'd thee: Judah, thy glory is departed, thy pow'r for hard captivity exchang'd! From heav'n to earth the Lord has cast thee down; Abroad the sword bereaveth, and within is death! O

Adagio. (♩= 88.)
a tempo Recit.

Thou, Al-might-y God, to whom a - lone we look for succour, Stretch forth Thine arm of pow - er, and save, O save Thy chos - en na - tion.

f col canto

Aria.
Larghetto con moto. (♩= 50.) *p espr.*

Re - mem - ber, Lord! re - mem - ber, Lord! what Thou hast laid up - on us; Our in - her - it - ance, our in - her - it - ance Thou hast giv'n, hast giv'n to

strangers. O where-fore, Lord, dost Thou for-sake Thy peo - ple? O where-fore, Lord, dost Thou for-sake Thy peo - ple? And why dost Thou for-get us for ev - - er? Re-turn, re-turn un-to Thy ser - vants, and their

strength do Thou renew, and their strength do Thou renew, renew, as in time of old. Remember, Lord! Remember, Lord! what Thou hast laid upon us; Our inheritance, our in-her-it-ance Thou hast giv'n, hast giv'n to strangers.

O where-fore, Lord, dost Thou for-sake Thy peo-ple? O where-fore, Lord, dost Thou for-sake Thy peo-ple? O why dost Thou for-get us for ev - - er? Re-turn, re-

cresc.
turn unto Thy servants, return, return unto Thy
cresc.
f
servants, and their strength do Thou renew, and their
f
p calando
strength do Thou renew as it was in time of
dim.
p
p
old, in time of old.
pp
poco rit.

The Crucifixion.

Aria.

J. STAINER.

King ever glorious! King ever glorious! The dews of death are gath-'ring round Thee, Up-on the Cross Thy foes have bound Thee, Thy strength is gone, Thy strength is gone! Not in Thy Maj-es-ty, Robed in Heaven's su-prem-est splen-dor; But in weak-ness and sur-ren-der, Thou hang-est here.

Who can be like Thee? Pi-late, high in Zi-on dwelling? Rome, with arms the world com-pell-ing? Proud tho' they be, Thou art sub-lime,— Thou art sub-lime!

Far more aw-ful in Thy weak-ness, More than king-ly in Thy

meek-ness, Thou Son of God, Thou Son of God.

Glo-ry, and hon-or: Let the world di-vide and take them; Crown its mon-archs and un-make them; But Thou,— Thou wilt reign.

Here in a-base-ment, crownless, poor, dis-robed, and

bleed - ing; There in glo - ry inter - ced - ing; Thou art the King! Thou art the King! There in glo-ry in-ter-ced-ing, there in glo-ry in-ter-ced - ing; Thou art the King! Thou art the King! Thou art the King!

The Daughter of Jairus.
Aria.

J. STAINER.

hope is in the Ev-er-last-ing, that He will save you; and joy is come un-to me from the Ho-ly One, be-cause of the mer-cy which shall soon come un-to you from the Ev-er-last-ing, our Sav-iour, our Sav-iour.

I sent you out with mourning and weeping, I sent you out with mourning and weeping, But God will give you to me again with joy and gladness, with joy and gladness, for ev-er, for ev-er.

165

I sent you out with mourning, but God, but God will give you to me again with joy and gladness, with joy with joy for ever, for ever, for ever, with joy, with joy, with joy, with joy. My hope is in the Ev-er-last-ing, that He will save you, and joy is come un-to me from the Ho-ly One, be-cause of His mer-cy which shall soon come to you from the Ev-er-last-ing, our Sav-iour, joy is come to me, joy is come to me, be-cause of the mer-cy which shall soon come to you from our Sav-iour.

The Light of the World.
Aria.

Sir A. S. SULLIVAN.

Andante moderato.

con molta tenerezza

Re-frain thy voice from weep-ing and thine eyes from tears, for thy work shall be re-ward-ed, saith the Lord. Re-frain thy voice from weep-ing and thine eyes from tears, for thy

cresc.
work shall be re - ward - ed, saith the Lord.
cresc.
p
And there is hope in thine
p cresc.
cresc.
f
dim.
end, that thy chil - dren shall come a - gain to their own
fp
cresc.
bor - der, and there is hope in thine
cresc.
end, that thy chil - dren shall come a - gain to their own

p
bor - der. Re - frain thy voice from weep - ing
p
and thine eyes from tears; thy work shall be re - ward - ed,
cresc.
cresc.
saith the Lord. There is hope in thine
p
p
end, that thy chil - dren shall come a -
cresc. molto
cresc. molto
gain. Re - frain thy voice from weep - ing and thine
ff
con passione
ff

eyes from tears, for thy work shall be rewarded, saith the Lord. Refrain thy voice from weeping and thine eyes from tears, thy voice from weeping and thine eyes, thine eyes from tears.

The Prodigal Son.

Recitative and Aria.

Sir A. S. SULLIVAN.

No chastening for the present seemeth to be joyous, but grievous; Nevertheless, afterwards it yieldeth the peaceable fruit of righteousness: For whom the Lord loveth, He chasteneth, And scourgeth ev'ry son whom He receiveth.

Aria. Andante con moto. (♩=76)

Come, ye children, and hearken unto

me, I will teach you the fear of the Lord. Come, ye children, and hearken unto me, I will teach you the fear of the Lord, I will teach you the fear of the Lord.

Lo! the poor cri-eth, and the Lord hear-eth him; Lo, the poor cri-eth, and the Lord hear-eth him, yea, and sav-eth him out of all his trou-ble.

Lo, the poor cri-eth, and the Lord hear-eth him.

Come, ye children, and hearken unto me, I will teach you the fear of the Lord, O come, O come, and I will teach you the fear of the Lord. Come, ye children, hearken unto me.

Harvest Cantata.
Recitative and Aria.

C. M. v. WEBER.

Look how the fruit-ful land is smil-ing, Wher-e'er we turn our eyes; A ver-y garden, tend-ed by the Lord.

Recit.
p
Fair shew the happy val-leys; up-on the meadows flow'rs are num-ber-less; while
dolce
con rigore
cresc.
gold-en ears of corn are rich-ly wav-ing, and orchards thick-ly hang with mel-low
con rigore
f
fruitage. The might-y sun from out earth's bosom calls the seed to new-found life and
cresc.
Recit.
beauty; the Prince that o'er the kingdom wise-ly reigns, and gives us peace, makes labor end in
f
plen-ty. O Fa-ther-
a tempo
f

177

land! Both heav'n and earth com-bine their pow'rs for thee, and make their blessings thine.

Aria. Allegro. (♩ = 120.)

Hap- -py na- tion, still re-ceiv-ing Gifts from Na- ture's lov- ing hand! Hap-py na- tion, still o-bey-ing One that wise-ly rules the land; Hap- py na- tion, still o-

15830

bey-ing One that wise-ly, that wise-ly rules the land,__ One that wise-ly_ rules the land.

Let us praise_ our gra-cious Fa-ther, Whose un-er-ring coun-sel_ gave One that just-ly, mild-ly, wise-ly, O-ver us_ the rule should have, Let us praise our gracious Father, Whose unerring counsel gave One that justly, mildly, wisely, Over us the rule should have, over us, over us the rule should have. That which kindly Nature

sends us, Toil to sure per - fec - tion
So the
most de-
cresc.
brings; So the joy that most de-lights us From sin-
p cresc.
cere en-deav-or springs, So the joy that most de-lights us From sin-
cere en-deav - or springs.
Hap - - py na-tion, still re-

-ceiving Gifts from Nature's loving hand; Happy nation, still obeying One that wisely rules the land, One that wisely rules the land, that wisely, that wisely rules the land, that wisely rules the land, that wisely rules the land, that wisely rules the land!